The Hamster's Diary

and Other Kinds of Writing

compiled by Brian Moses

Oxford University Press 1992

Oxford University Press, Walton Street, Oxford OX2 6DP

Oxford New York Toronto
Delhi Bombay Calcutta Madras Karachi
Petaling Jaya Singapore Hong Kong Tokyo
Nairobi Dar es Salaam Cape Town
Melbourne Auckland

and associate companies in
Berlin Ibadan

Oxford is a trade mark of Oxford University Press

This collection © Brian Moses 1992
Published by Oxford University Press 1992

A CIP catalogue record for this book is available from the
British Library.

ISBN 0 19 916549   1

Typeset by Pentacor PLC, High Wycombe, Bucks
Printed and bound in Belgium

Contents

Fun with Lists

Judith Nicholls

Ten words which are fun to say...

bamboozle
dodo
flip-flop
cacomistle
poppycock
peapod
pimple
shillyshally
pterodactyl
WHIZZ!

(Further choices: giggle, hobbledehoy, hoi-polloi, skulduggery, lollipop, snivel, gobbledygook, thingummajig...)

Ten beautiful words...

murmuring
lingering
lonely
windblown
rain-washed
sighing
rosemary
swallowtail
firefly
lush

(Extras: waver, golden, wanderer, drift, lull, dewberry, speckled, dragonfly, whispering, misty, rosebay willow herb... last one's a slight cheat!)

Eleven words to use instead of said...

mumble
grumble
mutter
drone
grunt
stutter
yell
moan
snivel
groan
squeal

5

Ten words to call your mum when you want a pocket-money rise...

wise
wonderful
marvellous
thoughtful
reasonable
tremendous
just
genius
exceptional
rich

Ten things to eat beginning with G...

grape
greengage
groundnut
gooseberry pie
gravy
garlic ice-cream*
ginger biscuit
goulash
Granny Smith apple
Garibaldi biscuit

*They make it in California, honestly!

Under Our Settee

Martyn Wiley

4 lego bricks (different colours)
10 pence
Matchbox car (Volvo)
Ball of fluff
Dog's bone
Baby's sock
Half a custard cream
Library book (*Postman Pat's Rainy Day*, 2 months overdue)
Paintbrush
Today's paper
A green crayon

In Our Garage

Martyn Wiley

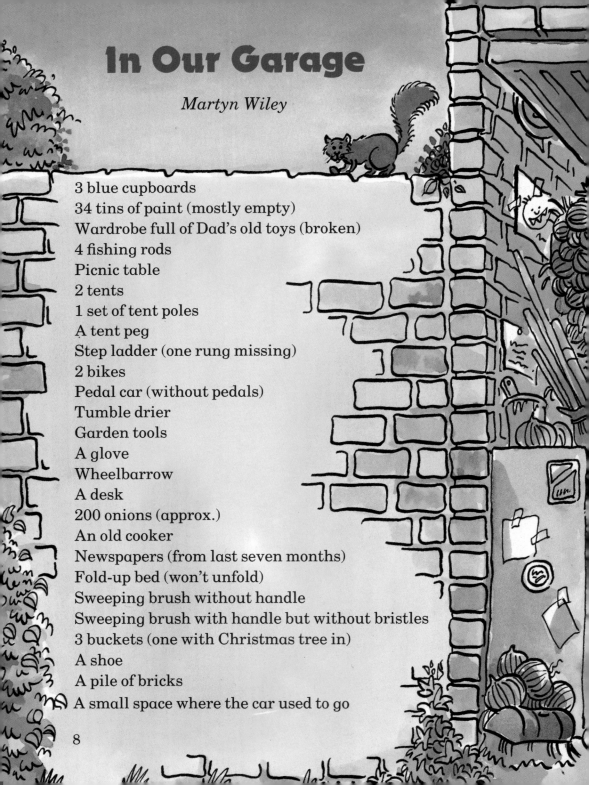

3 blue cupboards
34 tins of paint (mostly empty)
Wardrobe full of Dad's old toys (broken)
4 fishing rods
Picnic table
2 tents
1 set of tent poles
A tent peg
Step ladder (one rung missing)
2 bikes
Pedal car (without pedals)
Tumble drier
Garden tools
A glove
Wheelbarrow
A desk
200 onions (approx.)
An old cooker
Newspapers (from last seven months)
Fold-up bed (won't unfold)
Sweeping brush without handle
Sweeping brush with handle but without bristles
3 buckets (one with Christmas tree in)
A shoe
A pile of bricks
A small space where the car used to go

To Make a Sandcastle

Alan Brown

You need a bucket and spade,
and a lot of damp sand. Also lolly
sticks and wrappers for the flags.

Here's what to do.

Dig a hole and get in it. Throw
sand up all round to make walls.

Fill your bucket with damp sand
and turn it upside down on top of
the wall. Give the bottom of the
bucket a bash with your spade.
Lift up the bucket. Amazing! A
turret! Make some more.

Push the lolly sticks into the turrets. Wind a wrapper round each stick to make a flag.

Tunnel *very carefully* under the walls to make a way in. Dig all round the outside to make a moat.

Try to fill the moat with water from your bucket. Does it run away as fast as you put it in? Are the walls falling down?

Yes, that's what happened to mine.

Surprise-Your-Mum-Mocha-Chocca-Trifle

Irene Yates

This trifle is incredibly impressive, nobody will believe you've made it yourself!

Here's what you need:

Two chocolate swiss rolls.
Two packets of Chocolate Angel Delight.
One packet of Dream Topping.
Three quarters to one pint of milk.
Three teaspoonsful instant coffee.
Mug of hot water.
Whipped cream for decoration.
Chocolate Flake for decoration.

A mixing bowl.
A mug.
A whisk or electric mixer.
A large spoon.
A trifle dish, large. (This pudding is so delicious you always want to make a lot of it!)

First of all, break the swiss rolls into quite small pieces and place them in the bottom of the trifle dish.

Put the instant coffee into the mug of hot water and stir until it's dissolved. Pour the coffee over the swiss roll. Leave to cool.

Empty into the mixing bowl the two packets of Angel Delight and the packet of Dream Topping. Pour about three quarters of a pint of milk into it and whisk. Leave it to set for two or three minutes and then test the texture. It should be like a mousse, firm but soft. If it's not soft enough, add some more milk and whisk again.

Pile the mixture on top of the cooled swiss roll. Decorate with whipped cream, crushed chocolate flake and anything else you fancy.

You can cool this trifle in the fridge for an hour if you wish, but it should be eaten as soon as possible before the chocolate mixture 'collapses'.

Serve with a smile on your face and stand back because people will **rush** for it, it is so good. Make sure you get a dishful for yourself!

13

Recipe for Making Parents *Shout*

Martyn Wiley

You will need:

A puddle
Some soil
A small spade (if not, hands will do)
A younger brother or sister

Method

Wait until rain stops.
Ask to play outside (best to ask 20 or 30 times).
Outside, find a medium size puddle.
Get soil from garden and add to puddle.
Mix well.
Repeat until puddle is thick, black and sticky.
Walk through puddle (3 or 4 times).
Let younger brother or sister stand in puddle.

Then

Walk into house (best if everyone else is upstairs).
Run through every room shouting the words,
'Come and look at this'.

This recipe always makes adults shout but
works best if your house has pale coloured carpets.

Disco Party Invitation

Gina Douthwaite

To the Owner of That Dog

Wes Magee

Dear Neighbour,

Your dog has been in my garden pond
again. Really, enough is enough!
Yesterday, I found him swimming round
and round the pond smashing the lily
pads and scaring the living daylights
out of my goldfish. You *must* keep
him under control. I insist!

When he saw me coming he started to
bark like a lunatic. I tried to grab
his tail but missed. I fell into the
water. I was soaked, soaked to the
skin! Really, enough is enough!
Next thing I know he's out of the
pond and leaping the garden fence.
I stood there, in the pond, with a
goldfish wriggling on top of my head.

P.T.O.

16

Perhaps you remember the time he got into my kitchen. I'll merely remind you of the damage he did to my cornflakes, pickled onions, sausages, cheese and cream crackers. The worst moment was when I stepped on a packet of butter he'd been chewing and went headlong under the kitchen table. Really, enough is enough!

If you don't keep that wild beast under control I'll be forced to call the police. . . or buy a large shot-gun. It's either that, or stocking the pond with a dog-eating shark! That will teach him a lesson.

Yours, in great anger,

Mr Goldfisher

Letters from the Seasons

Ian McMillan

Dear Spring,

It's cold here. The weather has been terrible. It snowed for days and nobody could get out of the house. When it stopped snowing the children went out and built a huge snowman in the corner of the garden. There's still a little bit of snow left in the shade. The new baby stays in the house most of the time, and I can hear her crying.

See you soon,

Yours sincerely,

Winter.

Dear Summer,

It's lovely here. The weather has been fine. It was windy last week, though, and it blew some slates off the house. When the wind dropped the children came out and played in the garden. They've got a sandpit, it's a huge one, and they keep it in the corner by the hedge. The baby sometimes comes out and lies in her pram, and I can hear her laughing.

See you soon,

All the best,

Spring.

Dear Autumn,

It's hot here. The weather has been lovely. It was so hot last week that some people stayed in the house, where it was cooler. The children came out and played in their paddling pool. It's a huge one, and they've moved the sandpit to fit it in the corner of the garden. The baby sits outside all the time, and I can hear her trying to talk.

See you soon,

Keep smiling,

Summer.

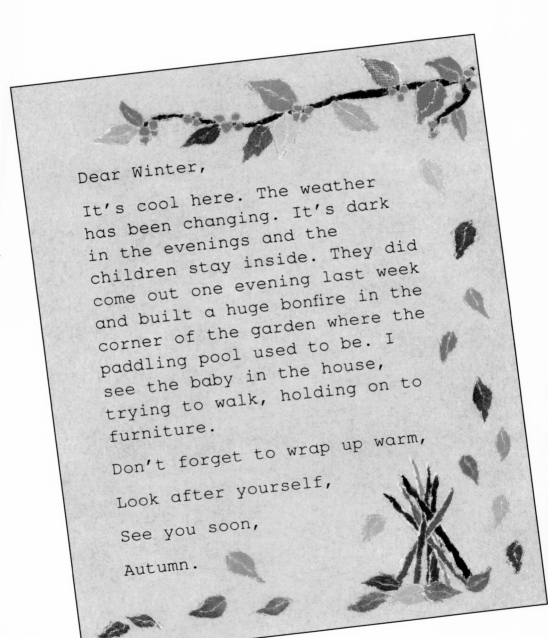

Dear Winter,

It's cool here. The weather
has been changing. It's dark
in the evenings and the
children stay inside. They did
come out one evening last week
and built a huge bonfire in the
corner of the garden where the
paddling pool used to be. I
see the baby in the house,
trying to walk, holding on to
furniture.

Don't forget to wrap up warm,

Look after yourself,

See you soon,

Autumn.

21

The Hamster's Diary

Martyn Wiley

11pm	Wake up.
11:30pm	Get out of bed.
Midnight.	Walk around cage.
1 am	Eat breakfast (nuts again)
2 am	Re-arrange sawdust.
3 am	Start jogging on wheel.
4 am	Still jogging on wheel (needs oiling)
4:30 am	Soon be fit enough for London Marathon (hamster section)
5 am	Large human crashes downstairs, switches on bright lights. Human RATTLES CAGE and SHOUTS. He is wearing striped suit tied with string.
7 am	Feeling tired, get into bed.
7:30 am	Large and small humans come downstairs. They shout, play music, punish eggs in boiling water and cut up bread with a knife.
9 am	Humans disappear. Peace. Sleep.

Froggy Tan

A HOLIDAY couple uncovered a slippery stowaway when they returned from a trip to Africa, a tiny tropical frog they named Kermit.

But in the winter chill John and Carole Harvey found that Kermit, who hopped unnoticed into their suitcase in Gambia, was about to croak. So Carole introduced him to her sunbed and he perked up immediately.

'It's amazing he survived at all after travelling hundreds of miles at 45,000 feet. He's a little battler,' said Carole, of Morley, Leeds.

Now Kermit is settling in at a tropical aquarium centre near Leeds where Carole will visit him with her grandchildren.

Scene Stealer

PEOPLE glancing over Monkbretton Bridge in New Road, Rye, during the past few days have been surprised to see a whiskery face with huge brown eyes gazing back at them.

A young seal has been spending a lot of time in the tidal River Rother. It has been catching eels and other fish, and has been a big attraction for children on their way to and from Freda Gardham School.

It is rare but not unheard-of for a seal to visit the river.

There is a fishmarket only yards from where the seal has taken up residence, but a spokesman could not say whether people were buying extra fish to throw to the seal.

The Giant Awakes

Stanley Cook

It was like an earthquake. The giant was waking up after his
long sleep. It had been a very long sleep, since someone of such
extraordinary size needed an extraordinarily long sleep – years
in fact. He shook the birds out of his long curly hair where they
had perched as if on the twigs of trees. He sneezed and blew the
rabbits out of his nostrils where they had been sheltering.
During his very long sleep seeds had rooted where the wind had

blown dust into the creases in his clothes. When he stretched himself whole gardens of flowers fell off him. Deer that had been nibbling the flowers slithered down his sides. Bats that had been hanging from the linings of his pockets flew away in alarm. When he stood up the fox that had climbed onto the toecap of his left boot had to jump to safety.

The giant slowly walked away from his resting place, leaving a deep, wide hollow where his enormous weight had pressed down the ground. Next time it rained, water collected in the hollow, and every time it rained the water that had gathered grew deeper and wider till it became a lake. People who rowed their boats across it named it after the giant who once slept there – Maximus Lake.

The Cool School Game

Trevor Harvey

For 2 to 38 players. You need counters and a dice – and a teacher who doesn't notice when you play games instead of working!

START

6 You remember that you have left your sandwiches at home. Return to START and collect them.

1 **Home.** You are in bed. The alarm-clock rings. You get up and go to the bathroom.

2 Your older sister is in the bathroom already. She takes *ages*. Miss two turns.

5 You run to the Bus Stop. Unfortunately, the bus is later than you are – so you manage to catch it. Forward two places.

3 You get washed and dressed, then you go downstairs.

4 You have some cereal and watch Breakfast TV. You pretend you don't hear your mum saying, 'It's getting very late...'

1 School. You arrive at your school. Unfortunately it is still there.

15 Lunchtime. You kick at a football, but you miss an open goal. Go to 16 and have another try.

8 The caretaker tells you that it's a 'Day Closure'. Go back to START (and to bed).

14 English. Your teacher asks you to write a poem about your favourite time at school. You write about hometime. Your teacher is not amused – so it's back to the Head's Study (10)!

9 You get caught eating sweets in the school corridor. Go to the Head's Study (10).

13 Playtime. You eat the apple your mum gave you for your teacher. Miss being called 'Teacher's Pet' – and miss one turn through stomach ache.

10 The Head's Study. Stand outside and miss two turns (and registration).

11 Assembly. You trap air in your armpit and make a rude noise. Go back to the Head's Study (10) and wait outside.

12 Maths. You use your calculator but still manage to get all the wrong answers. Your teacher says this is a record! Miss three turns.

16  You kick at the football again. This time, you not only miss the goal, you miss the football as well! Never mind.

17 You fall over in the playground and cut your knee. Go to the School Secretary (22) who says, 'What do you expect me to do – kiss it better?' No sympathy!

18 **Art and Craft.** You hide the box of scissors and the staple-gun. After ten minutes, the teacher stops searching for them and reads poems to the class instead. Forward three places!

19 **P.E.** The teacher tells you to balance on one foot. You do – but it belongs to the person next to you! Get sent to the side, to sit and watch for three turns, then go to 24.

23 **Story time.** You sit in the book corner and pinch Roger's elbow and pull Rosie's hair. The teacher sends you to the corridor. Go to 21.

22 The School Secretary gives you a message to take to all the classes. Miss the rest of the afternoon's lessons! Go to 25.

21 The Head walks by and says she wants to see you tomorrow. Go to the School Secretary (22) to make an appointment.

20  **Singing.** You tell the music teacher that you have a sick note. (She doesn't ask you to sing it.) Forward two places.

24 There is Swimming Club after school but you have forgotten your swimming costume *and* your towel. Miss catching a cold.

25 Hometime. You collect your coat and gallop down the school steps. Unfortunately, you miss your footing. . . Go to hospital (30).

26 You get a shock. Your mum has arrived to collect you from school – but all the other kids go home on their own. You hide in the toilets, until you think she has gone away.

27 Your mum is outside the school gates. She has brought you your towel and swimming costume. You are going to catch a cold after all!

30 Home. You have something to eat, watch TV, play with your computer, eat too many sweets, are sick – and then go to bed. You will soon be ready for another day at school! Return to START.

OR

Hospital. You have broken your leg and must miss school for the whole term! Find some better games to play. . .

29 Bus Stop. The bus is late again. You miss *Neighbours* as well as *Blue Peter*.

28 You are halfway to the Bus Stop when you find out you have put on the wrong coat. Go back and find the right one (25). . . Okay?

Acknowledgements

The editor and publisher are grateful for permission to reproduce the following copyright material.

Alan Brown, 'To Make a Sandcastle', © Alan Brown 1992. Reprinted by permission of the author. Stanley Cook, 'The Giant Awakes', © Stanley Cook 1992. Reprinted by permission of the author. Gina Douthwaite, 'Disco Party Invitation', © Gina Douthwaite 1992. Reprinted by permission of the author. *Early Times*, for permission to reprint 'Froggy Tan' from *Early Times* November 30 – December 6 1989, No. 99. Trevor Harvey, 'The Cool School Game', © Trevor Harvey 1992. Reprinted by permission of the author. Wes Magee, 'To the Owner of That Dog', © Wes Magee 1992. Reprinted by permission of the author. Ian McMillan, 'Letters from the Seasons', © Ian McMillan 1992. Reprinted by permission of the author. Judith Nicholls, 'Fun with Lists' ('Tens'), © Judith Nicholls 1992. Reprinted by permission of the author. *Rye Citizen*, for 'Scene Stealer'. Martyn Wiley, 'The Hamster's Diary', 'In Our Garage', 'Recipe for Making Parents Shout', and 'Under Our Settee'. All © Martyn Wiley 1992. Reprinted by permission of the author. Irene Yates, 'Surprise-Your-Mum-Mocha-Chocca-Trifle' © Irene Yates 1992. Reprinted by permission of the author.

The publishers would like to thank the following for permission to reproduce photographs:

Bruce Coleman Limited pp.24–25.

The illustrations are by: Bucket pp.12–13; Bob Dewar pp.22–23; Paul Dowling pp.4–5, 6; Honor Dry pp.16–17; Ann Johns pp.8–9; Jan Lewis p.14; Bethan Matthews p.7; Diana Mayo pp.26–27; Kimmy McHarrie pp.18–19, 20–21; Chris Smedley pp.28–29, 30–31; Reneé Williams pp.10–11.